Starting FROM THE Bottom

An interactive guide
to your first 90 days at work

SARVENAZ MYSLICKI

First edition September 2020

Book design by Laura Martín and Pablo Franco
Illustrations by Laura Martín

ISBN 978-0-578-75233-4

Never give up on a dream just because
of the time it will take to accomplish it.
The time will pass anyway.

Earl Nightingale

The road to
Success belongs to

To my husband Stephen, for joining me at the bottom and climbing with me ever since.

Note from the Author

There is a beautiful mountain in Austria called Untersberg. The hike takes about 4 hours, or you can pay to take a lift and be up in 15 minutes. The view at the top is the same, so why not just take the lift and save some time?

I'll tell you why – the experience. Only the hike can guide you through unforgettable pockets of nature, and bring your senses to life.

When you start from the bottom, the anticipation of the long trek ahead is almost palpable. The chill of the musty forest air seems to penetrate you to the bone. It is only with patience and steady movement that your body begins to warm itself.

At some point, the first warm rays of sunlight reach your face, snapping you out of the playful thoughts that were helping you pass the time. You notice how sparse the trees have become, and that the air is suddenly dry and sweet. The moss and damp soil has been replaced by grass and flowers.

Eventually trees become bushes, and then all that lies ahead are rocks and meadows. With the sun's heat on full blast, you get a glimpse of your final destination.

As you take your final steps to the summit, it becomes obvious why the hike is the better option. The view at the top might be the same, but it doesn't feel the same. The rest taken at the top feels better because of your aching muscles. The food eaten at the top tastes better because you're famished. The view looks better at the top because you've noticed its gradual transformation. In the end, you cherish the entire hike, not just the brief moment you sat on the peak.

Always appreciate the path to your destination. If you took a gruelling climb while someone else took the lift, know that once you both get to the end, your unique experiences will have made the entire journey worthwhile.

All the best on your journey,

Sarvenaz Myslicki

The map to your Journey

Start

Table of Contents

Before the 1st. Day

↓

The Total Package ————————————

In a typical job offer, salary gets the most attention, but don't forget all the other benefits.

Does your offer include:

Signing Bonus

◯ yes   ◯ no   How much? _____

Do you have to pay this back if you leave the company within a certain amount of time?

◯ yes   ◯ no

Relocation Bonus

◯ yes   ◯ no   Lump sum, moving services, or other? _____

Vacation Days

◯ yes   ◯ no   How many?_____

401k Matching?

◯ yes   ◯ no   How much? _____

Education/Tuition Assistance?

◯ yes   ◯ no   How much per year? _____

Student Loan Debt Assistance?

◯ yes   ◯ no   How much per year? _____

Health

General   Dental   Vision

◯ yes   ◯ no   ◯ yes   ◯ no   ◯ yes   ◯ no

Other: _____

_____

_____

If part of your package doesn't meet your expectations, don't be afraid to request changes. Negotiation isn't just for executives and used car salesmen!

Answer these two questions to prepare yourself in negotiating changes to your offer:

Why is it warranted? Explain why it's a reasonable request.
What do you want? Be specific and to the point.

 **Sample Situation**

There is no relocation assistance, but it will be a huge cost for you to move.

Sample Request

Since I am moving across the country for this position, I would like to request a relocation bonus of $5,000 to be included in the offer.

DON'T
Apologize for asking

DON'T
Go into unnecesarry detail

DON'T
Get too personal with your reason

Is there anything missing from your offer? Follow the template below and ask for a change.

Why is it warranted? _____

_____

What do you want? _____

_____

Your request (be as concise as possible):

_____

_____

_____

_____

_____

Bare Minimum Logistics ————

It's every new hire's biggest fear: the alarm doesn't go off, the dates got mixed up, traffic is horrible - the list goes on. It doesn't take much to spoil a first impression, so here are three steps to mitigate these worst-case scenarios.

Step 1: Re-read everything

Gather all emails or documents the company has sent you about your first day. Use them to fill in the details below:

My start date is ————————————————.

I am expected to arrive at ————————————. My goal is to arrive 15 minutes

earlier than that, which is at ————————————.

I will be meeting ———————————————— at the following location:

————————————————————————————————

My main contact's phone number is ————————————————————.

I was asked to bring these documents/items on my first day:

- ○ ————————————————————————
- ○ ————————————————————————
- ○ ————————————————————————
- ○ ————————————————————————

*Check them off once you put them in your bag

Step 2: Do the math

$$\frac{\text{WAKE UP}}{\text{TIME}} = \frac{\text{``GOAL''}}{\text{ARRIVAL TIME}} - \left(\text{TIME TO GET READY + DRIVING TIME} + \textbf{15 } \text{MINUTE ``VISITOR'' DELAY}\right)$$

Note: The "visitor" delay is especially relevant in high security facilities. A typical welcome desk is only staffed to process one visitor at a time, and there is often paperwork involved with getting temporary access to the building.

Minimize your "time to get ready"
Even if you have a stable routine, consider additional ways to save time by picking out your outfit and preparing your breakfast the night before.

Calculate your driving time

Best option: On the same day of the week and same time of day, do a test drive to the office. This will give you a sense of traffic, construction, and potential detours.

Alternative option: Using the Google Maps "Arrive by" setting, set the date and time you will be traveling and note the typical time range. Use the upper range as your estimate.

Fill in your numbers

| _____ | = | _____ | - (| _____ | + | _____ | +15 min) |
| WAKE UP TIME | | "GOAL" ARRIVAL TIME | | TIME TO GET READY | | DRIVING TIME | |

Step 3: Always set 2 alarms for day 1

Which 2 will you set?

| My phone | Spouse's phone (thanks spouse!) | Smart home device |
| Traditional alarm clock | Wake up call | Other |

Get a Head Start ————————————

Once you start your new job, you will be bombarded with information about your day-to-day responsibilities, and it will be hard to set aside time to learn about the company as a whole. By researching the items below ahead of time, you might even come in with more company knowledge than existing employees!

Check off as many of these as you can to get a head start:

○ Read the company's Annual Report.
○ Set up a news alert for the company.
○ Learn about the company's overall industry.
○ Learn about the company's top competitors.

Some on-the-job skills take a while to develop. If you have downtime before your first day, use one of the options below to ask your future manager if there is anything you can start learning ahead of time.

Option 1: Have an introductory call with your manager

In addition to asking about tools or skills to learn, you can ask about a typical day on the team, team structure, team processes, and details about your assignment.

What else are you curious to know? _____

_____

Option 2: Send a concise email your manager

→ **Sample template**

Dear _____

I am excited to be joining your team on ___**[INSERT START DATE]**___. *In the meantime, I'd love to learn more about any tools or skills that may be beneficial to me in the role. Let me know if there is anything you recommend I look into ahead of time.*

Thank you,

_____

Pop quiz

Fill out the information below to make sure you have the right foundational knowledge about the company and team you are joining:

The company

_____ was founded in _____. It is in the _____ industry and sells/produces _____.
The CEO of the company is _____, and has been in the position since _____. The company has _____ employees and made _____ in annual revenue in the previous year.
Is the company publicly traded? If so, what is the current share price? _____

Other facts about the company:

_____

_____

_____

_____

_____

The team

My manager's name is _____ and my role on the team
will be _____. My department's purpose is

_____

Other facts about the team:

_____

_____

_____

_____

_____

_____

Prep Your Presence ——————————

Your presence will influence the overall impression you leave on others. You can think of presence as a combination of your words, actions, attitude, and appearance. Here are some ways to prep your presence for your new position:

How you look

Don't make assumptions about the dress code

Dress code can vary by department. Within the same company, jeans could be the norm in one department and unheard of in another. Before you go on a shopping spree, get a sense of the dress code in the department you are joining, and check it off below:

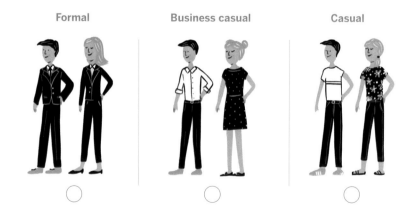

| Formal | Business casual | Casual |

Cut back on the "noise"

Think of noise as anything that could be distracting to others. Examples include bracelets that jangle every time you move your arm or excessive body spray.

Improve your posture

Good posture is not only important for conveying confidence, but also has long-term health and mobility benefits.

While the internet has a myriad of exercises for improving posture, you can keep it simple with these two fundamentals:

→ **Strengthen:** Build up the muscles in your back.
→ **Lengthen:** Stretch the muscles in your chest and shoulders.

How you sound

Eliminate your fillers

Um, so, like, you know? Words like these, which don't add any meaning to a sentence, are filler words. Filler word habits are often developed because they give the speaker time to think about what they want to say. The problem with fillers is that they "water down" your sentences and distract from your message. Depending on how frequently you use fillers, you could even be branded as a poor communicator. Therefore, it's important to find out your most common filler words, and start replacing them with natural pauses.

Listen to yourself

Most people don't enjoy listening to recordings of their own voice, but it is one of the best ways to discover "weird" speech tendencies. To test this out, record yourself answering the prompt below, which will come in handy on your first day:

⟶ Introduce yourself to your new team. Include information like your name, education, skills, and hobbies.

Listen to the recording and take notes on the following:

Fillers: _____

_____

Tone: _____

_____

Inflection: _____

_____

Speed: _____

_____

Pace: _____

_____

Customize your checklist

What other tasks do you want to make sure you do before your first day?

Task	Due Date

Write it out

Before the 1st day
What feelings come up when you think about your first day?

_____

_____

_____

_____

What would the ideal first day look like for you?

_____

_____

_____

_____

After the 1st day
What were the most memorable moments?

_____

_____

_____

_____

What would you change if you could repeat the day?

_____

_____

_____

_____

During the 1st. Week

↓

Meet & Greet

On page 19 you practiced introducing yourself. Once you learn more about your team and your assignment, start adding these details into your introduction. This way, you can make unexpected connections with people across the company who are familiar with your team. You will also benefit from the extra credibility that comes from having an early grasp on your assignment.

→ **Sample summary**

I work in the operations department, and my assignment is to create a new training program for our customer service agents.

Add your own summary:

_____

_____

Understanding your organization's structure will help you make important connections between the people you meet.
To start, map out the reporting hierarchy from yourself all the way up to the CEO.

Next, map out all of your manager's peers. These are people who report to the same person that your manager reports to.

Optional: Use the notes section in the back of the book to continue mapping out your organization's structure throughout your first 90 days.

You will meet a lot of people during your first week. To make sure you don't immediately forget names and other important details, jot them down here!

Name	Position	Department	Interesting Fact or Note
Sally Mae	Sr. Analyst	Marketing	We went to the same college

Office Survival 101 ———————

Offices can be very maze-like at first. In the excitement and commotion of my own first day at work, I went to the bathroom and completely forgot where my desk was. I was left wandering the halls until I ran into someone who knew where I sat. To prevent this from happening to you, make a note of the following:

My desk/cube number is _____ on the _____ floor.

Conference room technology is an enigma to some employees. Don't let this be you! During your first week, find an empty conference room and conduct a practice run of connecting to a virtual meeting. Better yet, read any available instructions for troubleshooting common issues, and you might save the day and make a great impression in an upcoming meeting.

Get all administrative activities out of the way while your workload is still light:

- ◯ Connect to a printer
- ◯ Set up your email signature
- ◯ Request access to tools used by your team
- ◯ Complete mandatory training
- ◯ Fill out HR forms and payroll
- ◯ Other: _____
- ◯ _____
- ◯ _____
- ◯ _____
- ◯ _____
- ◯ _____
- ◯ _____
- ◯ _____
- ◯ _____
- ◯ _____

Sometimes, managers are pulled into urgent situations and can't be around during your first week as much as they would like. If this happens and you've already finished all the tasks from the previous page, keep busy with the tasks below. You will come across as proactive, independent, and eager to learn!

• Have individual meetings with every member of your team to learn more about them and their role.
• Ask for any team and project documentation you can read through.
• Start joining relevant meetings, and take detailed notes in all of them.
• Look for any introductory or small tasks you can start helping with.

One of the fastest ways to make an impact on your new team is to write down all the unspecified tasks you had to complete during your onboarding process, and create a "new hire guide" specific to your team. Usually companies will have a generic guide, but it will be missing the steps that are only relevant to your team.

List down any activities that would make useful additions to your team's "new hire guide":

✓ _____
✓ _____
✓ _____
✓ _____
✓ _____
✓ _____
✓ _____
✓ _____

Write It Down, Look It Up ───────

Every company has its TLAs: Three Letter Acronyms. Within the same company, you might even find that the same acronym has two different meanings depending on the department! As you listen in on meetings and review documents, start to log the different acronyms you hear, and what they mean:

Acronym	What It Stands For	What It Means

Curiosity and a fresh perspective are two of the best traits in new hires. It will be important to question why certain things are the way they are and look for opportunities for improvement. However, when it comes to making suggestions for change, take the time to investigate your ideas from multiple angles before pitching them. Keep track of your ideas below and expand on them until they are "fully baked."

Ideas for change

What Exists Now	My Idea for Change	Benefits of My Idea	Drawbacks of My Idea

"We already tried that."

Even if you find out that your idea has been attempted before, don't let that discourage you from investigating further. Find out why the idea didn't work well the first time, and whether it is worth trying again.

What a Manager Wants ———————————

Everyone has a unique communication style. During your first meeting with your manager, figure out their style and fill in the information below:

• For urgent issues, my manager wants to be reached by: _____
• For everyday questions, my manager wants me to ask using:

Email	Phone	Text	IM	In Person	Other
○	○	○	○	○	○

• For updates and information, my manager wants me to share using:

Email	Phone	Text	IM	In Person	Other
○	○	○	○	○	○

• My manager wants to be updated every _____ ○ days ○ weeks on the status of my project.

Based on your manager's style, consider (or ask directly) whether they prefer updates that are more summarized or more detailed.

The pros/cons of each include:

	Summarized updates	Detailed updates
PRO	You save time up front.	They are more educated up front.
CON	If they have extra questions it will take longer for them to get the information.	Potential for wasted effort if they don't care about full details.

Note: This communication style activity works well with entire teams as well. Consider having everyone share their preferences and contact information in a centralized place.

Definition of done

For every task or project you are assigned, make sure you create a "definition of done" with your manager. For example, if you are asked to evaluate a process and make it more efficient, you might think "done" means that you have finalized and presented the new process. However, your manager might think "done" means that you have trained the operations staff on the new process and that everyone is actively using it. There is a big difference between the two! Knowing your end goal is critical to estimating timelines and setting the right expectations.

What is your project summary?

_____

_____

_____

_____

What is the end goal of your project?

_____

_____

_____

_____

Express your desire for feedback

Your ability to get high-quality feedback early and often is a key factor for success in your first 90 days. In an early conversation with your manager, let them know that you are excited to learn from them and that you value their feedback.

Then, get in the habit of seeking out useful feedback by keeping track of activities that are new to you, and referencing those activities instead of asking generic questions like "How am I doing?"

Here are some examples:

- "What do you think of the first draft of my process map?"
- "What did you think of my presentation today?"
- "How was my level of engagement in our team meeting?"

During the 1st. Month

Goals

The best goals are SMART goals: Specific, Measurable, Achievable, Realistic, Timely. Even more important - they should target the *root* of a problem. Let's use the example below to see this process in action:

Scenario: Clients are unhappy with the reports that they receive on a weekly basis.
Bad goal: I want clients to be happy with their reports.
This is a bad goal because you don't know the root of the problem: why are the clients unhappy? Whenever this happens, it is best to make your first goal to discover the root of the problem.
New (but still bad) goal: I want to send a survey to each of our clients to understand what can be improved about the reports.

This goal is better, but it is still missing some of the SMART criteria:

- **Specific:** You specified who (each client), but what about specifics surrounding the survey and number of improvements?

- **Measurable:** How will you know if you have conducted a successful survey?

- **Achievable:** Is it possible to get each client to take the survey? 100% response rates on feedback surveys are not very common.

- **Realistic:** Is it realistic for you to send something directly to clients? Some companies have experienced associates who are the only ones allowed to interact with clients.

- **Timely:** By when do you want to have the results?

Final (good) goal: Within the next month, I want to create a brief (no more than 10 questions) survey, receive clearance to send the survey to at least 80% of our clients, and get a response rate of at least 60%. With the responses, I want to identify and propose the top three areas of improvement for our client reports.

Creating good goals is not always easy or straight-forward, but it is an important step to make sure your work is meaningful and will add value. The process forces you to plan ahead, consider whether you're tackling the right problem, and create objective criteria by which to measure your success.

Use the chart below to create three SMART goals for your first 90 days. Make sure your manager is involved in the creation of these goals, and that meeting these goals will mean that you have met their expectations.

First, list out the three goals in their most basic form (like the "bad goals" from the previous page).

1. _____

_____

2. _____

_____

3. _____

_____

Next, add the details you need to make them **SMART**!

	S	M	A	R	T
1					
2					
3					

Map It

When you are first introduced to a project or assignment, it's important to map out the people who are involved in completing it (participants) and the people who care about the outcome (stakeholders).

Let's focus first on participants. Using the table below, list out all known participants and how they are involved.

Participant's Name	Participant's Organization	Participant's Role

Next, let's focus on stakeholders. It's important to note that caring about the outcome of a project doesn't mean that someone supports a project. You might actually find that some of your stakeholders don't agree with your project, or are negatively impacted by it. For example, you might be improving a process, but to the operations staff who are well-versed in the old process, you are introducing change that will disrupt their day-to-day activities.

Using the table below, list out all known stakeholders and how they are impacted by the project.

Stakeholder's Name	Stakeholder's Organization	Impact to Stakeholder

Note: If you can't identify any stakeholders other than the person who is assigning you the work, this is a potential sign that your project is not going to be very impactful. Talk to your manager to see if there are any hidden stakeholders, and get their perspective on the impact of your assignment.

Plan It

Even if you aren't in a project manager role, you will need to become the project manager of your own goals. This means planning the tasks, dependencies, and milestones needed to reach your goals and tracking them over time.

Let's break down the three key elements of your project plan:

Tasks can be obvious, like those explicitly assigned by a supervisor, or non-obvious, like the need to win over an unhappy stakeholder. Ideally, you should be able to complete a single task on your list in less than one week. If you have a task that you expect will take more than one week, try to break it down into smaller sub-tasks.

In the spaces below, write down the obvious and non-obvious tasks that come to mind for your project.

✓ _____

✓ _____

✓ _____

✓ _____

✓ _____

✓ _____

✓ _____

✓ _____

Dependencies are tasks that need to either start or finish before other tasks can start or finish. Sometimes you will be your own dependency (you can't proofread your first draft until you finish writing it) and sometimes one of your project participants will be the dependency (you can't write the report summary until a team member sends you the detailed analysis). Take a look at all the tasks you listed above, and circle or draw lines connecting any that have dependencies.

Milestones are like mini-goals. They mark significant achievements on the way to completing the overall project. Milestones should always have dates associated so you can tell if you are making fast enough progress toward your main goal. Using the timeline on the next page, fill in your tasks in order and label the completion of any major tasks as milestones.

Date	Task/Milestone

Log It

How you spend your time at work is useful to analyze. You might find out you are spending most of your time on activities that don't have any long-term benefits. Once your work-week starts to become steady and no longer filled with onboarding activities, log one week of your activities using the table below:

	Monday	Tuesday	Wednesday	Thursday	Friday
9.00 am					
9.30 am					
10.00 am					
10.30 pm					
11.00 am					
11.30 am					
12.00 am					
12.30 am					
1.00 pm					
1.30 pm					
2.00 pm					
2.30 pm					
3.00 pm					
3.30 pm					
4.00 pm					
4.30 pm					
5.00 pm					

What type of activities took up most of your time this week?

What were your most useful activities?

What activities do you want to reduce?

What activities do you wish you had more time for?

In addition to analyzing your time, you should set aside time once a week to log the accomplishments and tasks that you completed. This includes things like helping others accomplish their tasks, learning new skills, and one-off requests from your manager. These everyday activities can be easily forgotten otherwise, and it's helpful to have this list handy when it comes time to summarize your accomplishments for formal performance reviews.

Use the list below to log your tasks and accomplishments:

Date Completed	Work Completed

Days 30 through 90

Monitor Your Progress ⎯⎯⎯⎯⎯⎯

A common mistake that associates make after setting their goals is to file them away and forget about them until their performance reviews months later. By then their real work might have completely diverged from their goals. Even though they've performed well, they have failed to complete their original objectives. Your goals should be kept somewhere that makes them easy to access. Set a reminder to review them once a week, ideally at the same time that you plan your to-do list. This way, you can make sure you are focused on doing the right tasks in the right order of priority.

Over time you might find that the tasks being assigned to you no longer match up with any of your goals. When that happens, you'll want to speak with your manager about whether your goals should be updated. Don't let this scare you. There is a big difference between updating goals and not meeting your goals.

Updating a goal is required when business priorities change and you are asked to shift your focus. This can happen quite often in the business world, and shouldn't be seen as a bad thing. Resist the urge to keep your original goals and add on top of them. It's almost always more impactful to exceed expectations for a smaller number of important goals, than to meet expectations on a massive list of items while burning yourself out. When a new goal comes in, an old goal comes out! Be sure to document any part of your old goal that you already completed, so you can still get credit for it.

Not meeting a goal is when priorities don't change, and you start falling behind on the progress you thought was possible. It could be any number of reasons: you forgot a dependency, you underestimated the difficulty of a task, you made a mistake, etc. In situations where you are at risk of not meeting your goals, the sooner you bring it up to your manager the better. The worst thing you can do is try to make everything look like it's running smoothly, only to have everything surface toward the end. The best associates bring up risks right away, with a plan for mitigating them.

Effective risk mitigation relies on two key factors:

1. Being able to quickly sense when things are going wrong. This ability improves with experience, so until you gain that experience, it's best to plan for the worst by default. Even though it takes extra effort to plan for scenarios that might never happen, this practice will put you on the same playing field as more seasoned employees.

2. Having the creativity and/or the connections to fix the problem. This is especially true in large corporations, where your ability to complete a task might require you to track down someone with a very specific skill set. Sometimes you'll need your creativity for solving complex problems, and other times you'll need it simply to figure out "how do I get this person to answer my emails!"

Use the table below to help you with your own risk mitigation strategies:

Week	Risk Description	Mitigation Plan
July 13 – July 17	Person completing dependecy task is out sick and won't be able to finish according to plan	Option 1: Ask if someone else on their team can finish the task. Option 2: Learn more about the task so I can do it myself. Option 3 (last resort): Inform stakeholders that there is risk of a delay.

Learn Your Lessons ————————————

Making mistakes when you are new might not feel great, but there is no better time to mess up. I have rarely felt as much stress as I did in my first 90 days out of college, because I could not stop making mistakes! My project kept getting delayed, my solution was being poorly implemented, and I was in way over my head with extra commitments I didn't know how to get out of. It turns out I had a manager whose style was to let new hires make mistakes instead of "saving" them, because he knew that feeling of messing up was much more powerful than being lectured to. Those lessons became so ingrained in my brain that I've never made them again. I've since stolen his techniques, and will let my new hires make (safe) mistakes, knowing it's not a pleasant experience at the time but that nothing will set them up better for learning their lessons.

Sometimes we get lucky and our mistakes don't cause any negative outcomes, or are quickly forgotten. Even if that is the case, it is important to retrospect whenever a mistake is made. Use the questions below to guide you in these reflections:

What happened? _____

_____

How did you react? _____

_____

What was the impact of the mistake? Could it have been worse?

_____

_____

What decisions or factors contributed to the mistake being made?

_____

_____

How will you prevent yourself and others from making this mistake in the future?

_____

_____

Some lessons are not learned as a result of making mistakes, but by figuring out better ways to do things over time. These are harder to notice because the improvements are gradual, and they rarely get documented against the original, less effective ways of working. This is why in some departments, especially ones that are process-heavy, the more seasoned staff will have found ways to do things better, but these "insider tips" never make their way back into the training documents for new employees.

Get into the habit of writing down the improvements you make over time. No matter how obvious the improvement seems at the time, the key is that it was not obvious in the beginning. Don't make every newcomer learn the hard way!

Use the space below to list out improvements you've made and advice you would give to others who end up in a similar role as yourself.

1. _____

2. _____

3. _____

4. _____

5. _____

6. _____

7. _____

8. _____

9. _____

10. _____

Find Your Mentor

Finding a mentor is an important step for professional growth. A mentor can help you learn from their mistakes, provide career guidance, expand your network, and so much more. When starting somewhere new, it can be hard to know who to approach and how to initiate a mentor/mentee relationship.

One of the best ways to identify a mentor is to find someone who was recently where you are now, and ended up where you want to go next. For example, a great mentor for an intern would be a past intern who was was able to successfully receive a full-time offer at the end of their internship.

In the spaces below, write down the names of people who were once in a position that is similar to the one you are in now. This could be anything from having the same title to simply being a new hire.

1. _____   4. _____

2. _____   5. _____

3. _____   6. _____

Of these people, list up to three who have accomplished something that lines up with your own aspirations. This could be anything from winning a prestigious award, getting a promotion, or something intangible like maintaining work/life balance.

1. _____ Accomplishment: _____

2. _____ Accomplishment: _____

3. _____ Accomplishment: _____

Next, pick one person that you want to approach first. There is no need for a grand "Will you be my mentor?" proposal. A simple email along the lines of "I would love to grab lunch and learn more about..." is a great way to start. Because you are the one seeking guidance, it is up to you to prepare meaningful topics ahead of time. Answer the following questions to help you think about what you want out of the discussion:

1. What is your goal for the session?

_____

_____

2. What do you want your mentor to know about you?

_____

_____

3. What are some specific questions you want to ask?

_____

_____

_____

Depending on the formality of your meeting, you can choose to bring a notebook and take notes during the discussion, or you can make mental notes and jot them down as soon as the session ends. In both cases, you should be writing down what you learned! Use the space below to capture the notes from your first session:

_____

_____

_____

_____

One misconception about mentorship is that it has to be a structured, long-term commitment. Some mentorship programs are formally structured that way, but this is not required. You and your mentor could be living 2,000 miles apart, catching up sporadically via email every couple of months, or you could meet once a year at an annual conference. Both of these can be just as fulfilling and beneficial as a biweekly meeting.

Since mentees get so much value out of a successful mentorship, they often wonder what they can do to "give back" to their mentors. Here are three ways:

1. Put in the effort. Whenever a mentor shares recommendations, like improving a skill or researching a topic, treat it almost like mandatory homework.

2. Share the impact they have on you. Any time your mentor's guidance helps you, let them know! A quick message along the lines of "I took your advice to practice my elevator pitch and today I used it to impress the head of my department. Thanks again for your help!" will really brighten their day.

3. Pay it forward. Always seek to be a mentee and a mentor. As a new hire, your mentorship can help students and other candidates searching for their first job.

Exceed Expectations ————————

Every company has its own unique process for evaluating employee performance. At the most basic level, most of them use a scale like this one:

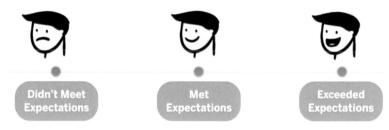

Didn't Meet Expectations · Met Expectations · Exceeded Expectations

Chances are, someone who is proactive enough to be using this journal is not content with only meeting expectations. This section is meant to help those who want to stand out as going above and beyond what is expected of them.
Let's first dispel the #1 myth of performance reviews: If I work hard, I will get a good performance review. This might be the case in a small team where everyone's contributions are evident, but in large, complex organizations, it's not that simple. Hard work is necessary, but the following steps are just as important:

Step 1: Understand the scale

This information is usually available via formal documentation that explains the different performance designations. Some companies will also set guidelines for the percentage of employees who can qualify for different designations. For example, they may designate no more than the top 20% of employees as "exceeding expectations." Another common element is having multiple factors make up the scale. For example, to exceed expectations overall, an employee may need to exceed expectations in a tactical category as well as a strategic category.

Step 2: Understand the process

This information isn't usually made available (often on purpose), so you may need to lean on your mentors for insights into this. For example, in some companies people other than your manager have influence over your performance designation. If this is the case, you want to make sure you invest the time to make a positive impression on these individuals. It is also important to know the timing of the process. If all performance reviews for the year are finalized in November, don't plan all your biggest contributions for December.

Step 3: Don't commit to exceeding expectations up front

There is a reason this is not in the same section as goal setting. Until you know more about the intricacies of your project, it will be hard to know where to exceed expectations. For example, if your original goal is to make a process run 20% faster, you might be tempted to think that making the process run 30% faster is a good metric for exceeding expectations. However, once you dig into the process you could find out that the bigger problem is actually the quality of the output, rather than the speed of the process. Therefore, a more impactful way to exceed expectations would be improving quality by 10%.

Step 4: Ask your manager what it will take

If exceeding expectations is a top priority for you, you need to be ready to confront your manager with direct questions about your performance. It is quite rare to have a manager who will point out exactly what it will take, because even they know that there is an element of uncertainty to the process. However, by forcing them to think about what exceeding expectations means to them, you are helping minimize the uncertainty. Be sure to document expectations-related discussion by sending a summary email after your meeting.

Once you've taken the steps above, use the space below to list some ways you can exceed expectations. You can pull inspiration from your original goals, tackle new problem areas you've discovered, or think about leadership activities that will give you exposure across the company. These leadership activities could include organizing a training session, presenting a topic you are well-versed in, or hosting a collaboration session for teams that would benefit from working together.

1. _____

2. _____

3. _____

4. _____

5. _____

6. _____

Day 90 and Beyond

Reflect & Adapt ———————————

There is great value in regular reflection throughout your career (and life) journey. Without taking the time to reflect and adapt, your personal and professional growth could go unnoticed and even start to stagnate. Instead of moving down a path that is fulfilling for you, you might end up at a dead end and feel completely lost.

Here's your chance to reflect on the past 90 days:

What tasks were most enjoyable for you?

_____

_____

What tasks were your least favorite?

_____

_____

What were your top 3 accomplishments?
1. _____
2. _____
3. _____

What were your top 3 lessons learned?
1. _____
2. _____
3. _____

If you could start your first 90 days again, what would you do differently?

_____

_____

_____

_____

_____

In what ways do you want to develop yourself in the next 90 days?

_____

_____

_____

_____

_____

What opportunities will you take on to develop these skills?

_____

_____

_____

_____

Now is a good time to meet with your manager and discuss your performance. Complete these three steps before arriving at the meeting:

1. Complete your own reflections first. You don't need to share them, but it will allow you to be more thoughtful when discussing your performance.

2. Think about specific tasks or behaviors for which you want feedback. List them out here: _____

_____

_____

3. When it comes to receiving feedback, be prepared to dig, rather than defend. A common response to critical feedback is to become defensive or make excuses. Instead, become a detective and dig for specific examples that explain why your manager feels a certain way.

Once you have your manager's feedback, capture it below:

What are your strengths?

_____

_____

_____

What are your areas of improvement?

_____

_____

_____

Write down any other feedback from your manager:

_____

_____

_____

_____

Interns: Final Days ————————————

For interns, the 90 day mark (or sooner) usually means the end of their internship. This section covers key activities when closing out an assignment, whether at the end of an internship, or the end of any other role.

Effectively transitioning a project is a valuable skill throughout your entire career. If you skip this step or don't leave enough time to do it properly, things tend to fall apart as soon as you leave them behind. This is especially true for interns, whose projects are at higher risk of being abandoned due to short transition periods.

There are two important steps in any transition:

1. Put relevant information in a readily accessible place.
Check these items off once you have properly documented them:
- A summary of your project
- Names and contact information of those involved in the project
- The benefits of your project
- Links to important resources
- A list of all tasks that have been completed
- A list of any tasks that are pending, guidance in how to finish them, and names of people who have agreed to make sure the tasks get finished
- A list of maintenance tasks that need to take place on an ongoing basis, and names of people who will complete these tasks

2. Make sure someone truly cares about your project.
All the information could be available but if no one is sold on the benefits of continuing your project, it will sit untouched. This is especially true with process changes. Due to the resistance to change, as soon as the change advocate leaves, the process users tend to revert to the old process.

The art of keeping in touch

A common practice during someone's last week at a company is to send an email to their co-workers saying farewell and sharing personal contact information. This is a nice gesture but it relies on other people being proactive in keeping in touch with you. If there are people you want to make sure you keep in touch with, you will have to take extra steps.

Step 1: Make sure you have a way to contact them. From least to most personal, these options include: LinkedIn, business email, personal email, and phone number.

Step 2: Set yourself a calendar reminder to connect. This doesn't have to be too often; every couple of months is a good cadence.

Step 3: Re-connect for a specific purpose. Don't force the interaction with a generic "How have things been?" email. Talk about a new project you're excited about, a special milestone in your career, or a specific problem you'd like their help with. If your reminder pops up and you can't think of anything specific to share, snooze your reminder for another time.

In the table below, list the people you want to stay connected with. Then, set a reminder to revisit this page in the future.

Name	Contact Information	Reason for Staying in Touch

Expanding Your Reach ———————————

Once you have established momentum and a high standard of performance in your main role, you are ready to start branching out to establish greater credibility in a wider network.

First, list out all employee resource groups, professional organizations, planning committees, and task forces that exist at your company.

_____

_____

_____

_____

Next, pick three that you want to get involved with. What is your motivation behind each of these?

1. _____ Motivation: _____

_____

2. _____ Motivation: _____

_____

3. _____ Motivation: _____

_____

In addition to volunteer and group activities to expand your network, it's useful to expand your knowledge of other teams and functions within the company. This not only gives you context for how your team fits into the overall company, but also makes you aware of the types of skills and experiences you would need to move into other roles within the company.

Some companies explicitly set aside time for learning new skills or collaborating on side projects not directly related to day-to-day tasks. If this is not the case in your company, consider setting aside some of your own time to explore. These activities are important for your career growth, and often help you develop skills you wouldn't get in your main role. On the next page, you'll find some methods to broaden your understanding, ordered from lowest to highest time commitment:

1. Eat lunch with at least one new person every week. It's easy to fall into the habit of having lunch with the same group of people. Even worse, you might feel so overloaded that you start working through lunch. Don't underestimate the value of lunch-hour networking!

2. Take an hour each week to learn about a new team or understand the purpose of another organization. Ways to do this include reading internal documentation, sitting in on another team's meetings, or scheduling time with subject matter experts.

3. Sign up for training sessions, special events, or discussion forums hosted by your company. If there are limited internal opportunities, check if your company has any policies that will pay for you to complete external training.

4. Take an idea that you believe in, research its benefits and feasibility, and either pitch it or build it. This can be an individual side project or, if others are interested, a collaborative group activity. If your idea is process related, like improving new hire onboarding, you are better off pitching the recommended changes to the relevant process owners. If your idea is product or technology related, like developing a script to automate manual tasks, you are better off building a prototype that can be demoed to the relevant product or technology leaders.

What are some ideas you believe in?

1. _____

2. _____

3. _____

4. _____

5. _____

6. _____

7. _____

8. _____

9. _____

10. _____

Continuing Your Journey ────────────

A successful first 90 days will set you up with great momentum as you continue in your role. Even though the next step in your journey could be months or years away, it's important to know the general direction in which you want to go. Use the prompts below to figure out your direction:

Within your company, list the roles that interest you:

_____

_____

_____

Within your industry, list the companies that you admire:

_____

_____

_____

Across all industries, list the careers that intrigue you:

_____

_____

_____

Within your company, what are the top 5 roles you know you don't want to take on next, and why? Knowing what you don't want can be just as helpful in guiding you.

1. _____

2. _____

3. _____

4. _____

5. _____

Get creative! Use the space below to draw a map of your future. It can cover the next 90 days or the next 10 years. It can be career-oriented or span multiple aspects of your life.

Everyday Tips

The Big Picture ———————

Due to the desire to make a good impression, new associates tend to dive into their day-to-day tasks and take on incoming work without questioning it. Weeks or months go by, and even though they have never missed a deadline and their manager is happy with them, they haven't found a sense of purpose in their work. This is where "big picture" thinking comes in handy. Follow the steps below to make sure the work you take on has value and genuinely makes a difference.

Step 1: Understand strategy at different levels

What are your company's goals? If you don't know where to find this information, ask your manager for help.

_____

_____

_____

_____

_____

What are your team's goals?

_____

_____

_____

_____

What connections do you see between your goals, your team's goals, and the company's goals? If you are having trouble making these connections, this makes for a great discussion topic with your manager.

_____

_____

_____

_____

_____

_____

_____

Step 2: Question your impact

Just because someone assigns you work, doesn't mean that work will add real value. Next time you get an assignment, do not start until you have answered the following questions:

Who will benefit from the work?

_____

What is the benefit of the work?

_____

_____

_____

What will happen if I don't do this work?

_____

_____

_____

The other big picture
The other big picture has nothing to do with goals and strategy. It is all about people. Ultimately, what you work on isn't as meaningful as who you work with. Project details tend to fade over time, but the connections you make will be the memories that stick with you.

You better recognize!
Receiving recognition is one of the most powerful motivators. Set yourself a reminder at least once a month to recognize the people around you who have done a great job. Use the space below to get started:

Name of person	What they did well
_____	_____
_____	_____
_____	_____
_____	_____
_____	_____

Email Etiquette

A huge portion of workplace communication still happens over email. You can't be a good communicator at work if you are not good at communicating via email.

One of the biggest misconceptions that new hires have is that people will read their emails. Most of the time, you are lucky if the recipient skims your email, especially if it is more than a couple sentences. Make it easy for others to digest your emails with these tips:

Convey purpose with the subject

One helpful format is ACTION: SUMMARY

→  **Examples**

Approval Requested: Design changes for product revision
Action Required: Travel budget due by end of the week
Feedback Requested: Client report final draft
Call for Volunteers: Monthly outreach event

Color-code emails meant for multiple people
Often, meeting notes are sent via email to summarize outcomes and action items. Whenever you are in charge of sending out notes, try to draft them in a way that lets each attendee quickly find what is relevant to them.

→  **Example**

Action items (list these ahead of general meeting notes):
All: send corrections to your respective budgets by next Tuesday
Sara: finalize marketing content before the next meeting
Philip: review document changes with legal team by the end of this week

Tips for every email

• Read the email twice and try to remove content on the second pass. You'll make your emails more concise and catch typos along the way.

• Leave the recipient field empty until you're ready to send the email to avoid sending a half-finished draft by accident.

• Never email while angry! If you find yourself drafting a harsh email while upset or annoyed, wait to send it until the next day. When you re-read it the next day you'll most likely be glad you didn't send it.

• Limit how often you "reply all." Replying to everyone on an email chain is a quick way to spam more people than necessary. In some cases, accidental reply all scenarios can even lead to sharing sensitive information with unauthorized people.

• Prevent unnecessary "reply all" by using the BCC option for large announcements.

Manage your inbox

Learning to manage your inbox will keep you organized and prevent your inbox from managing you! Here are some recommended techniques:

• Read emails in bulk - either three times a day (morning, noon, end of the day) or no more than once per hour.

• Only "touch" emails once. As you go through your emails, force yourself to do at least one of the following:

If no immediate action is required:
→ Delete it.
→ File it into the appropriate folder.
→ Create a rule/script that will delete or file similar emails in the future.

If action is required:
→ If you can reply or finish the action in less than 2 minutes, do it right away.
→ If it will take longer, flag or star it with a deadline associated.

Meeting Management ———————

I attribute a huge portion of my early career success to the fact that I became very good at running meetings. Surprisingly, few people know how to run effective meetings, so you have a chance to really stand out as a new hire by learning how to make the most out of your meetings.

There are two must-haves to send out with every meeting invite:

1. Explicitly stated purpose or goal. This lets your attendees know what to expect out of the meeting.

2. Agenda topics and time allocations for each item. Meetings without time allocations almost always run out of time before getting to all topics.

In thinking through these details you will also get a good sense of who the attendees need to be. For example, if your meeting goal is to make a decision, you need to make sure the right decision makers are invited.

Be a firm time-keeper
Usually when there is no one watching over the time, the people listed early in the agenda will get most of the time, and those at the end will get little to no time. There are friendly but firm ways to cut off people who have surpassed their allotted time. Something like "I'm going to move on to the next topic so that we have enough time to get through the agenda, and we can come back to this if time permits" works well.

Make sure everyone is heard

Take note of those who haven't been contributing and specifically ask if they would like to add anything. If you notice someone getting interrupted by another attendee, bringing the conversation back to them will mean a lot to them.

Take useful notes

A good note taker is very different from a scribe. Instead of capturing everything that is said, focus on these three items:

→ Note important decisions, who was in favor of each option, and why they were in favor of that option.

→ Note useful pieces of information that attendees will want to reference later on.

→ Note action items, who they are assigned to, and when they are due.

Use the space below to prepare for your first big meeting

Meeting date & time: _____

Meeting participants: _____

_____

Meeting purpose: _____

_____

Meeting agenda:

Time Allocated	Topic

No Fear

Successful careers require taking risks. Fear will get in the way of your ability to take risks. One way to embrace fear is to start with the worst-case scenario and then mitigate from there.

For example, if your worst-case scenario is getting fired because you can't support yourself financially without your job, you will need to tackle that first. Once you have more of a financial safety net, your "worst-case" is no longer as dire, and taking a risk at work no longer has the same consequences.

Try it out!
First, list out some activities (big or small) that scare you about work. They can be things like delivering a presentation, standing up to a pushy team member, or making a mistake that impacts your manager.

_____

_____

_____

_____

_____

_____

_____

_____

_____

_____

Next, circle your top three fears from the list above, and write out the worst-case scenarios that can happen in each situation.

1._____

_____

2._____

_____

3._____

_____

Finally, write out how you would tackle the worst-case scenarios.

1._____

_____

_____

2._____

_____

_____

3._____

_____

_____

You can continue this activity for a variety of scenarios, not just the worst-case. Starting with the worst-case is helpful because it will make all the other obstacles seem easier by comparison.

Too many people are thinking of security instead of opportunity. They seem to be more afraid of life than death.

James F. Byrnes

About

↓

The Author

Sarvenaz Myslicki is a technology executive who has spent over a quarter of her career in the "first 90 days" of different roles. By making the most of this critical time in a new role, she has been able to quickly maximize her impact and create confidence in her ability to take on new roles. Sarvenaz's love of mentoring and helping others succeed in their own careers was the inspiration for this guided journal. In her spare time, Sarvenaz is a non-profit leader, professional speaker, and certified yoga instructor.

The Designers

Laura Martin was born in Buenos Aires, Argentina, and is a graphic designer from the University of Buenos Aires. She specializes in digital and analog illustrations, as well as design and layout for print and digital publications. She loves to eat (but not cook!) and has a passion for reading fiction novels.

Pablo Franco is a designer with over 20 years of experience. In addition to specializing in digital product design, he is passionate about editorial design and unique projects that positively impact people's lives. This book was the perfect ground for expressing his commitment to helping new hires. In his spare time, he's an amateur sailor.

My notes

My notes

My notes

My notes

My notes

My notes